HANS KRESSE

Riders
of the
Wind

METHUEN · LONDON

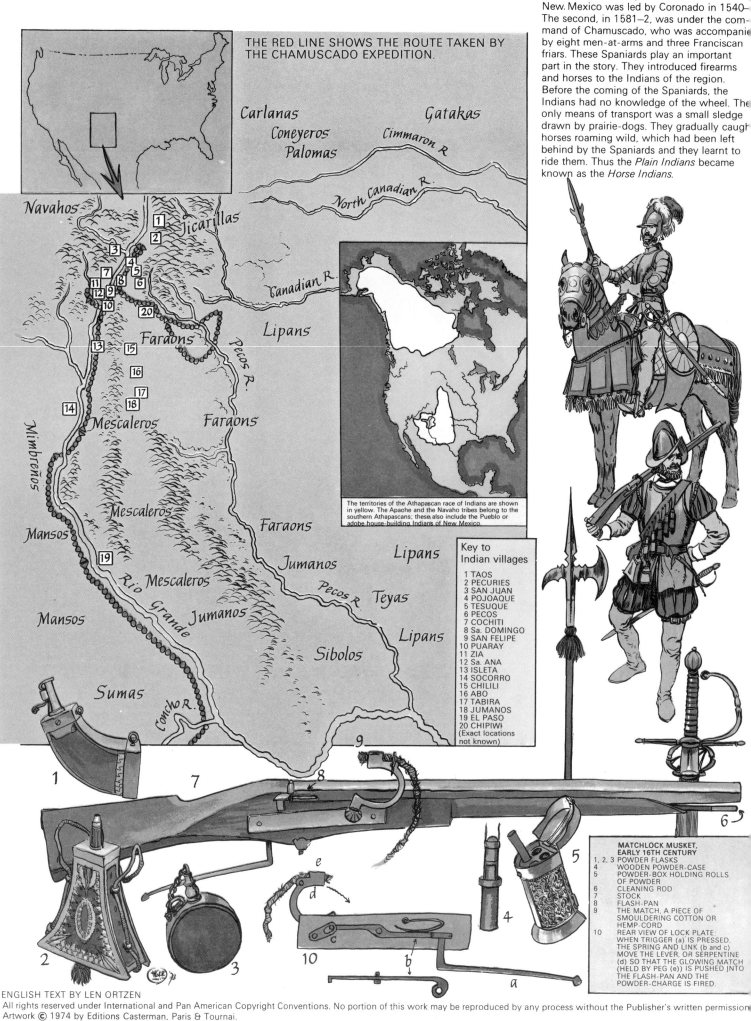

THE RED LINE SHOWS THE ROUTE TAKEN BY THE CHAMUSCADO EXPEDITION.

The first Spanish expedition into what is now New. Mexico was led by Coronado in 1540. The second, in 1581–2, was under the command of Chamuscado, who was accompanied by eight men-at-arms and three Franciscan friars. These Spaniards play an important part in the story. They introduced firearms and horses to the Indians of the region. Before the coming of the Spaniards, the Indians had no knowledge of the wheel. The only means of transport was a small sledge drawn by prairie-dogs. They gradually caught horses roaming wild, which had been left behind by the Spaniards and they learnt to ride them. Thus the *Plain Indians* became known as the *Horse Indians*.

Carlanas
Coneyeros
Palomas
Gatakas
Cimmaron R.
North Canadian R.
Navahos
Jicarillas
Canadian R.
Lipans
Faraons
Pecos R.
Mescaleros
Faraons
Mimbrenos
Mescaleros
Faraons
Mansos
Jumanos
Lipans
Rio Grande
Mescaleros
Teyas
Mansos
Jumanos
Lipans
Sibolos
Sumas
Concho R.

The territories of the Athapascan race of Indians are shown in yellow. The Apache and the Navaho tribes belong to the southern Athapascans; these also include the Pueblo or adobe house-building Indians of New Mexico.

Key to Indian villages

1 TAOS
2 PECURIES
3 SAN JUAN
4 POJOAQUE
5 TESUQUE
6 PECOS
7 COCHITI
8 Sa. DOMINGO
9 SAN FELIPE
10 PUARAY
11 ZIA
12 Sa. ANA
13 ISLETA
14 SOCORRO
15 CHILILI
16 ABO
17 TABIRA
18 JUMANOS
19 EL PASO
20 CHIPIWI
(Exact locations not known)

MATCHLOCK MUSKET, EARLY 16TH CENTURY

1, 2, 3 POWDER FLASKS
4 WOODEN POWDER-CASE
5 POWDER-BOX HOLDING ROLLS OF POWDER
6 CLEANING ROD
7 STOCK
8 FLASH-PAN
9 THE MATCH, A PIECE OF SMOULDERING COTTON OR HEMP-CORD
10 REAR VIEW OF LOCK PLATE: WHEN TRIGGER (a) IS PRESSED, THE SPRING AND LINK (b and c) MOVE THE LEVER, OR SERPENTINE (d) SO THAT THE GLOWING MATCH (HELD BY PEG (e)) IS PUSHED INTO THE FLASH-PAN AND THE POWDER-CHARGE IS FIRED.

ENGLISH TEXT BY LEN ORTZEN

Artwork © 1974 by Editions Casterman, Paris & Tournai.
English Text © 1975 by Methuen Children's Books Ltd., 11 New Fetter Lane, London EC4P 4EE.
First published in Great Britain 1975. ISBN 0 416 55450 4

*See 'The Masters of Thunder'

They're right above us! Oh brothers, forgive our foolishness!

The bearded warriors are back?

It must have been their animals making so much noise. But I fear something else.

The thunder people came at the same time. Does that mean the bearded warriors are truly masters of thunder?

I'm cold with fear, Little Fox. The tracks lead towards our camp.

Wait! What can we do against the might of the bearded warriors and the thunder people?

But we must go to the help of my father Chaka!

All right, but stay hidden. If we're too late to help our brothers, we can warn the other tribes.

Perhaps we could—

That noise again!

HIHIHIHIHIHi HIHIHIHIHi

The bearded warriors... coming this way! Quick, hide!

??

* Indians who lived in villages.

* The Creator of the universe according to the Apache.

Sita: father
Siye: son

We should be mightier than our enemies, sita, and swifter than the buffalo.

Uh-huh!

That's why I want them. Is that a thing to be laughed at?

No, little warrior. Only a fool laughs at things he doesn't understand.

If we had these creatures we could load our goods on their backs, too!

And go faster and farther.

Yes, but how would you catch them?

And how would you train such wild creatures? Even dogs don't always obey us!

No, and we don't sit on them.

If the strange warriors can do it, we can.

If no one else dares, let me try, father.

My warrior brother has too much imagination.

He speaks the language of youth. Only the old can understand it.

They're coming straight at us! They'll trample us down.

Something has scared them — wolves...or enemies.

Look...warriors!

No, they're turning away. Aren't they swift!

Too swift for you, Little Fox.

Quick, hide!

They took cover when they saw us. There are only two.

Only two? They must be Togua scouts (1)

Or Roa's (2) braves - not knowing who we are.

We'll find out. Come on.

WOH WOHWOHWOH WOHWOH!

The call of the wolf! They must be Roa's braves. There's some danger.

(1) Togua or Jumanos tribe.
(2) Chief of another Apache tribe.

WOHWOHWOH WOHWOH!

Here they come.

Why are they afraid?

Bad news! The Toguas have raided the camp of Roa and slaughtered our people!

Ahagaha! What about Roa, my blood brother?

He was with us and some squaws gathering mescal* away from the camp. We escaped only because night fell, but Roa is wounded. Help us get him to safety!

* A plant, basic food of the Apaches.

Roa heard you, brother, and you're wrong.

My squaw is dead, my grandson too. I must live to avenge them.

He has a brave heart. May the Great Spirit help him...

Prepare a stretcher for him, you squaws.

WHO'S THAT?

WOH WOHWOH WOH!

One of our scouts.

Toguas! Only a few hours' march away! Scores of them, and on our tracks!

14

They'll catch up with us – the wounded will slow us down!

We'll all be killed!

Who speaks of flight...or of death? Trust in Chaka and his braves!

The father of the tribe must be mad to think of fighting!

My elder son Unda speaks like a coward. Squaws flee, warriors fight!

Your son is right, brother. Fly! Give me a bow and arrows, and I'll delay the Toguas as long as possible.

Brave words but senseless, brother. You must think of living, not dying.

Is the stretcher ready? Take Roa to my camp. My younger son Anua will go with you.

No, I'm staying.

Children go with the squaws... I'm not one!

No, you're a warrior...but also the last son of the Faraon chief.

But perhaps you are right... You're a free warrior, free to live ...or die.

Follow the river, sisters. Warn my people.

What will Chaka do? We are so few...

Call in the scouts and I'll explain.

A few hours later, Two Togua scouts...

There are the cursed cantsi*

One is being carried. That must be Roa. Tell our chief, Kaloch...he wants to kill him with his own hands.

* Togua word for liars.

15

* Another Apache tribe, also called Jicarillas. See map.

* See Masters of Thunder

Unda sneers at me... We'll fight it out with knives one day!

Stop quarrelling! We're wasting time.

Anua is a free warrior. If he wants to warn the Chipewyans himself, that is good.

And Pashka, killer of panthers, will go with him.

Safe journey!

You look worried, Pashka.

Yes, your brother has spite in his heart. Chaka knows you have good sense and are protected by the gods. Unda knows that too...

...his spite will grow and then one day...

...I know, one day we'll fight.

That will be a terrible day for the chief, your father. If Unda kills you, I will kill Unda!

Don't let this happen. Promise!

And always be mocked... and taken for a coward? No, I must challenge him.

Think, brother! Don't act in haste. Now we must hunt for food.

A few hours later...

I'd like to cook this meat, but the Toguas are about. It's safer not to make fire.

If we have to fight, may the Great Spirit help us! But quarrels and strife between brothers anger the gods. Your pride can bring misfortune upon the whole tribe.

Then must I...

Listen! A man who masters himself, masters his greatest enemy. Control your pride, turn a deaf ear to your brother's spite, and the Great Spirit will help you and our people.

If your brother provokes you again, I'll step in...

CRACK CRACK CRACK

(1) *Buffalo-eaters, a nickname given to Apaches*   (2) *See Masters of Thunder.*

Otsani still alive? Impossible!

It's true. The trader from Cikuye* has seen him. But come into the village...

*The Pecos village. See map.

We will smoke the pipe of peace, and you will see Sapohi.

DOA!

No, we must start back at once. The Togua scouts cannot be far away, they must not see us.

Will you not eat? Wait, I'll have food brought to you.

Thank you no. We'll hunt on the way.

The wise hunter knows best. Go then, and give my greetings to your chief. Peace be with you.

My heart tells me something terrible will happen...

Why the hurry to leave? To avoid the Togua scouts?

Perhaps I was wrong... I don't know... I sense some disaster...

A few days later...

We've left the mountains far behind... not a sign of Tog-uas.

But here are their tracks!

They are fresh, too... and lead towards the shellfish river!

Look... vultures!

My heart is heavy. Vultures mean death.

Do you think the Toguas have raided the Faraon camp?

22

I fear so. We must go cautiously.

A little later.

Look...a dead body just outside the camp, and here... tracks of the Toguas.

No fires, no smoke to be seen...

Huh! It's a Togua.

More over there. But as they've left their dead, that means they had to flee...

Then why is the camp deserted?

There are no traces of blood

No, the tribe has moved on. There must be a message for us somewhere.

Yes, this twig! Look...it tells us which way to go.

To the north! To our brothers the Tashindes. And here are the tracks of our people.

A few hours later...

BANG!

Th-that's a thunder-stick! The bearded warriors! The tribe is in danger!

No, don't shoot! You will betray our presence and the bearded warriors can't be far away.

Ni...i...i...ih...

Don't kill it!

But this animal attacked you! And why did you shoot at the wolves? I told you not to!

Quick, come away! It's not safe. And there are none of our people here.

Help! Anyone there? Help!

* Half-breed, son of a Spaniard and an Indian woman.

Tell us how you got here. Then we'll know *who* we are helping.

It's a long story.

Faraons like long stories.

Well, I had to flee...

Flee? Had you done wrong?

I didn't think so, but the Span ...the bearded warriors did. I hit the chief man at the hacienda where I was working. He was evil, but still... hitting him was not allowed. As I had to flee, I stole a horse... not allowed either... and a firearm. They'd hang me if they caught me...

What do 'hacienda' and 'hang' mean?

An hacienda is a kind of village where animals are bred and maize is grown. Hang means having a rope tightened round your neck.

But then you can't breathe.

You're not meant to.

The bearded warriors are cruel. Why did you go and work at this ha-haci...?

Hacienda? I had to make my living.

Huh! We Faraons live without working for others. These bearded men have strange customs.

I agree, amigo. Well, I met four armed men making their way north, and I travelled with them...

They said they were looking for gold, but I think they were slave-traders. I would have left them if I could...

And I got the chance one day when they were about to raid a village... They gave me back my gun, and I escaped during the attack, though not without a shot in the shoulder and three arrows in my side.

Koh! So now we know all about you, what would you have us do?

Just help me on my horse. I think I broke my leg when I fell off.

Lift you onto your... animal?

Is that too difficult?

Thanks. I can manage now.

Aah, my leg! Won't one of you help me?

Wait Anua! I'll do it.

Ni...i... i...h

Now my gun ...I – I ...

He's sick. Take him to our camp, the old one will cure him.

The Chipewyans told us that Otsani and his son are with the Toguas.

What? Do they still live? The Tashindes will not help us, and the gods have turned from us. Are we to be wiped out by the Toguas?

We killed their scouting party, then we moved camp. But they will attack us one day.

Here come our braves. They have a prisoner – a bearded warrior!

In the Faraon camp...

Come and see the prisoner.

It's a bearded warrior, and he's wounded.

His animal has been captured, too!

Why does he still hold his thunder stick? That's dangerous.

Listen, my people! This man is our friend!

Now the medicine man has two wounded men to care for.

Take the reins and help me down, young warrior. Will you tend my horse and see he isn't eaten?

I'll do that for you.

Our friend takes more care of his horse than of himself.

Yes, horse first, rider second. He's my best friend. Now your medicine man can take care of me.

Haha! My young brother has to look after this animal... He's a servant now.. and to an animal!

Enough of that, Unda! The animal is the friend of my guest, so our hospitality extends to both. If my younger son wishes to look after the animal, he may do so.

His leg is not broken, but he has a small stone in his shoulder. I can get it out, then he'll be better. But Roa is very weak. He wishes to see you.

It gladdens my heart that you're here, brother. Death has been at my side. If I must leave for the happy hunting grounds, promise you will take my place...

I promise. But think of living, not leaving!

I had a dream, and in it I saw many mysterious animals running about the plains... and then there were Faraons on their backs. The thunder spoke... many Toguas appeared... and a great wind blew from the south... Then I woke up.

You have a fever, brother. Rest... I'll come back soon.

Strange...here's one of those animals, and Anua wants to sit on its back. Is that a sign?

How are you, friend half-breed? We saw four horses running wild on the plain...

Yes, four broke away. But about your young son, chief...

WOH... WOH WOH WOHWOH

Toguas are coming! As many as there are buffaloes on the plain!

BANG!

Now you'll see them run, ha-ha!

And our brothers run too!

Another shot after those Toguas and they'll run still faster!

BANG!

That's sent them off! It's all calm now friends! You can come back... and I can be ill in comfort.

Friend half-breed... You were sent to us by the Great Spirit, and we are in your debt.

?

Bah! Don't talk about it.

See how the tribe greets you... like a hero. How can we help you?

By making an enclosure for my horse to run about in. Otherwise he'll waste away, and what would become of me if he died?

It will be done, my friend. In a good spot where grass grows by a stream. And I think my younger son will gladly see to it.

And so he did.

You spend much time looking at this animal. If only it was of some use ...

What do you mean?

Oh nothing. Come, brothers, we'll go hunting. That's man's work.

Unda still sneers at you, Little Fox? Just say the word, and he'll feel the wrath of Pashka!

It's nothing. I think he believes I'm afraid to go near the horse.

It's very wild. Be careful.

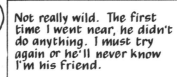

Not really wild. The first time I went near, he didn't do anything. I must try again or he'll never know I'm his friend.

Here's food, brother horse. Don't go away.

So that night ...

I've come to sit on your back, brother. Let me try ...

Stand still!

I'm up!

Huh!

?

Now move forward.

Go on!

Do you hear? Move on!

Good. N-not so fast. Now turn right.

To the right ...not into the water!

I'm disappointed in you.

Why didn't you turn when I said? I shall ask friend half-breed what to do.

Ni...i... i... ih...

In the morning... How are you? Better? Er... how does your horse know when to turn and when to go straight on?

What makes you ask?

Little warrior you always surprise me. You've been on his back, haven't you? I can tell from your face... Wait a little longer... I'll teach you to ride.

The mother is coming at me! What shall I do?

She wants help. Her foal is stuck in that swamp. But if you go nearer, you'll get stuck yourself!

Give me the rope. I'll see what I can do.

I've come to help you, little one. Don't be afraid. Now pull, half-breed!

Bravo, youngster! The mare has got her foal back... and you've got yourself a horse!

At the camp.

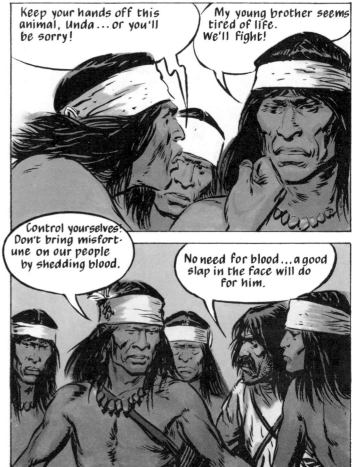

Will that do, chief?

Yes, you've won and the horses are yours.

Hm, but I'm depriving the tribe of food. That's not the way to make friends.

We have enough food... but you have made an enemy.

Now Roa is your friend and in your debt. You fought for me and saved the animals... can I see them?

Yes, they are handsome. Soon, I will be well so that I too can mount and be a rider of the wind.

Will he get well?

I despaired. But now I'm sure of my blood-brother's recovery ...his will to live has returned!

Truly they are wonderful animals.

Will you teach Roa how to ride?

Yes, I've plenty of time. I don't even know where I'm going.

Then why not stay here?

Doa! You have brought us much good fortune. Stay and become one of us.

Come quickly, chief! Your elder son is leaving and some of his comrades with him!

O foolish men! Think of the Toguas... we must be united against them!

Send away the stranger who humiliated Unda... then we'll return.

It is better that I should leave.

Chaka doesn't give way to threats! Go then... it is fated!

I know my son... he quarrels with everyone. His comrades will leave him sooner or later, and he'll be alone. He might escape the Toguas, but not his worst enemy... himself. If he conquers that enemy, then he will come back to us and be your friend.

Don't think of leaving, for we need you. You have to teach Roa to ride... and perhaps Chaka too!

But me first... on the young horse.

Very well. When the foal no longer needs its mother, we'll start.

Some time later

He's grown a lot, eh? Steady there... we are not going to harm him.

Go ahead!

Why are you walking like that?

He's as stiff as a post... and sore. But first attempts are always difficult.

I'd rather walk without pain than go fast and be sore!

But Anua persisted...

Bravo, youngster! You've mastered it! Look, chief... your son is the tribe's first horse-rider!

But he has still a lot to learn. And that can only come from practice.

Can we go to the Chipewyan village, sita? I could show Sapobi my horse and... and...

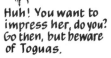

Huh! You want to impress her, do you? Go then, but beware of Toguas.

How can I watch over Anua now?

You must learn to ride, Pashka... as we all must.

Koh! See how well I'm riding him!

I can see you're not falling off!

What's that smoke?

The village is over there.

It's on fire and under attack!

By Toguas! We're just in time!

* The Lipan tribe of the Apaches, sworn enemies of the Faraons. See map

Printed by Casterman S.A., Tournai and Paris.

Continued in *Sons of the Chief*